Brooke
and
Her Crayons

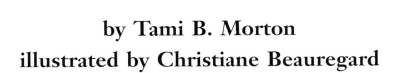

by Tami B. Morton

illustrated by Christiane Beauregard

 HOUGHTON MIFFLIN   BOSTON

Brooke had to have an operation. The doctor took out her tonsils. After the operation, it hurt Brooke to talk.

The next morning, Mom and Dad brought her some crayons and paper. They said that Brooke could draw pictures instead of talking.

Brooke began to draw pictures all the time.

Brooke drew pictures to ask for help. She drew pictures to tell things to her mom and dad. But most of the time, she just drew pictures for fun.

When Brooke was able to leave the hospital, she had a good idea.

"I'll leave my crayons here," she told her mom and dad. "Then someone else can use them too."

Brooke was a little worried about leaving the crayons behind. She still wanted to draw. Brooke had never liked anything so much.

When Brooke got home, she used things around the house to draw pictures. She drew pictures in the dirt with sticks. She drew pictures on the sidewalk with chalk. She drew pictures in the air with her finger.

8

Soon it was Brooke's birthday. Her mom and dad surprised her with a new box of crayons and lots of paper. Brooke was very happy!

Brooke practiced drawing every day. She practiced before school and after she finished her homework. She even practiced before she went to bed. Every time Brooke practiced, she loved drawing more and more.

Brooke continued to practice drawing until she was grown up. Then she became a wonderful artist and an art teacher.

Now Brooke goes to the hospital and brings crayons and paper to sick boys and girls. Maybe one of these children will grow up to be an artist and a teacher. Just like Brooke did!